JUL 2 9 2008

MAY 2 8 2008

DEMCO

ANTHOLOGY OF POETRY
BY
YOUNG AMERICANS®

2007 EDITION
VOLUME LVII

Published by Anthology of Poetry, Inc.

©*Anthology of Poetry by Young Americans*®
2007 Edition
Volume LVII

All Rights Reserved©

Printed in the United States of America

To submit poems
for consideration in the year 2008 edition of the
Anthology of Poetry by Young Americans®,
go to: anthologyofpoetry.com or

> Anthology of Poetry, Inc.
> PO Box 698
> Asheboro, NC 27204-0698

Authors responsible
for originality of poems submitted.

Anthology of Poetry, Inc.
307 East Salisbury • P.O. Box 698
Asheboro, NC   27204-0698

Paperback ISBN: 1-883931-67-3
Hardback ISBN: 1-883931-66-5

Anthology of Poetry by Young Americans®
is a registered trademark of
Anthology of Poetry, Inc.

Each year, we are fortunate enough to be able to spend a time walking the seashore and selecting the most beautiful shells from all those laid before us. So many beautiful creations are there for the taking! How does one choose from among them? They come in all different shapes and sizes. Some are outwardly beautiful, some require a keen eye to discern the intricate patterns hidden within. Each one is carefully crafted by a hand we shall never see, yet each gives us a glimpse into the heart and mind of its creator.

Dedicated educators from across the country have imparted their love of poetry to their eager students who have, in turn, created a small image of themselves in their work. The wonderful poems presented here in the 2007 edition of the *Anthology of Poetry by Young Americans*® represent the finest works of students from all across the country. Take your shoes off, dig your toes into the sand, and enjoy the beautiful shells we have selected for you.

For eighteen years now, we have had the privilege of showcasing the collective works of some of the country's finest young writers. We continue to receive letters of appreciation from teachers, students, parents, and grandparents. For these, we are truly grateful and encouraged. This year, we have added a feature which we believe will further enhance the quality of our publication: following this introduction, you will find a Registry of Authors which will help you locate your favorite authors. We hope you find this a useful guide as you explore the wonders set before you in the sand.

The Editors

Registry of Authors

WHAT HE SAID

I lay in bed at night
Praying that everything will be all right
Until one night I felt a hand on my shoulder
It was God's hand I felt
As a soft voice whispered
Everything will be OK
Everything happens a certain way
Everything takes place at a certain time
Life isn't as easy as making up a rhyme
Life has its courses
Life is going to be rough
But you, my child, you are tough
I created you, I would know
As His soft voice whispered
It was time for Him to go
Now I lie still in my bed
Thinking about what He said
I know life has its purposes
I guess it's just the way life is

Erica Vedell
Age: 15

AMERICA

Red, white, and blue, we honor you.
You are valuable to us too.
Through all the bombs bursting in the air,
our stars and stripes were still there.
We honor our veterans who fought for us,
we must show we care and not cause a fuss.
America, America we think you are great,
we love each and every state.
America we love you, red, white, and blue.

Madison Vershaw
Age: 8

THE NOTE

I wrote a note it was so sad,
  I wrote a note that was not bad.
I wrote a note I did not dread,
  I wrote a note and did not hang my head.
I wrote a note that made me cry,
  I wrote a note that made me sigh.
I wrote a note that made me think,
  I wrote a note that made my heart sink.

Lindsey Brown
Age: 9

Madness is red.
It smells like tuna.
It looks like fire.
It tastes like a tomato.
Madness feels like a crab pinching you.

Paige Elizabeth Meyer
Age: 9

Camping
noisy, fun
building, biking, fishing
campfire, boat, uniform, badges
hiking, swimming, playing
brave, easy
Boy Scouts

Brandon Taets
Age: 8

Dad
nice, special
loving, coaching, giving
football, baseball, best friend, fun
licking, barking, nipping
playful, curious
Puppy

Olivia Draminski
Age: 8

Miss Hamblin
pretty, smart
working, helping, trusting
She is the best.
Teacher

Shane Barr
Age: 9

Soccer
exciting, physical
passing, playing, running
friends, team, slide, twirl
lifting, jumping, singing
fun, microphone
Dancing

Samantha Lain
Age: 9

Tumbling
easy, tough
running, jumping, flipping
cartwheels, round offs, bat, helmet
tossing, catching, fielding
fun, challenging
Softball

Madeline Alepra
Age: 8

E lectrical
E xciting
L ong

Austin Murray
Age: 10

L ively
O cean creature
B iotic
S pineless
T ailed
E dible
R ed

Cole Busler
Age: 10

Frogs
tiny, rough
jumping, swimming, leaping
tree frog, bullfrog, dachshund, boxer
barking, walking, fetching
gentle, lazy
Dogs

Breanne Busboom
Age: 9

Happiness is yellow.
It smells like a pot of gold.
It looks like go, go, go.
It tastes like a flower-shaped plate.
It sounds like my mom baking a cake.
Happiness feels like a sweet pancake.

Amber Autrey
Age: 9

Happiness is yellow.
It smells like sweet fresheners.
It looks like a smiley face.
It tastes like bubblegum.
It sounds like laughing.
Happiness feels like having a blast.

Kyle Urish
Age: 9

Football
fun, rough
punting, scoring, running
player, field, bait, pond
casting, waiting, catching
lazy, quiet
Fishing

Trey Tessier
Age: 9

FIRST PLACE

It seems to me
    That I could never be
        First place

No matter how hard I try
    I could never be
        First place

I'm not talking about
    First place in a
        Show or competition

I'm talking about
    First place in your eyes

It seems to me
    No matter what I do
        It never pleases you

What do I have to do!?
    Jump through a flaming hoop
        While juggling bowling balls
            And balancing cake on my head?
Is that what you want me to do?

I'm sorry
    I'm only human
        I can only do so much

All I want to be
    Is first place
        In your eyes

            First Place

                Kelly Gale Masters
                Age: 13

D aring
O utstanding
L oving
P layful
H armless
 I ntelligent
N oisy
S ea mammal

                Britany Davidson
                Age: 10

9

FROGS

Slippery, slimy
They're so gross
Gooey, grimey
Now it's time dissect them.

Joe Gleason
Age: 10

HAPPINESS

Happiness is white.
It smells like goodness in the air.
It looks like a bright light in the sky.
It tastes like anything good and sweet.
It sounds like a sparkling noise.
Happiness feels like a soft warm blanket in my bed.

Ryan Johns
Age: 10

Paige
funny, nice
laughs, jokes, helps
Paige is so nice!
Best friend

Rachel Lee
Age: 9

Alex
nice, kind
walking, running, jumping
He is the best.
Brother

Adam Avery
Age: 9

Dakoda
Funny, kind, hyper
Daughter of Beth and Dan
Sister of Ian, Mia, Amber, and Logan
Loves horses, family, and food
Fears dark, falling from heights, things squishing me
Wants to see Goliath and Lady Liberty
Lives in Green Valley, IL
Tharp

Dakoda Tharp
Age: 9

Wild horse
interesting, mammal
running, speeding, sprinting
I love this animal.
Pony

Morgan Thompson
Age: 10

J elly-like
E legant
L ucid
L ovely
Y ikes!
F ree-swimming
I nteresting
S hocking
H anging tentacles

Meredith Wheat
Age: 11

S limy
Q uick
U gly
I ntimidating
D angerous

Alex Avery
Age: 11

SLY BEAR

Then I saw a bear,
Sitting right there beside me,
Eating on my hair!

Abbie Miller
Age: 9

Zebras
fast, striped
grazing, walking, galloping
like sheep in a meadow
Peaceful

Caleb Ulick
Age: 10

M agnificent
A crobatic
N oiseless
T hin
A ctive

R eally big
A dventurous
Y oung grow quickly

Hannah Mangan
Age: 10

M ost wonderful animal
O f the zoo. I'm
N ot trying to
K id around, and they also
E at a lot of bananas.
Y es, they are very cute!

Rayanda Coziahr
Age: 9

Happiness is yellow.
It smells like flowers.
It looks like smiles.
It tastes like candy.
It sounds like laughing.
Happiness feels like joy.

Stephanie Miller
Age: 9

ANOTHER OLD LADY WHO LIVED IN A SHOE

Their was an old lady who lived in a shoe,
And an old man that lived there, too.
So they sat down with the flu,
And drank stew.
Their names were Lou and Drew.

Camden Brown
Age: 9

Thrilled is pink.
It smells like singing.
It looks like dancing.
It tastes like hip-hop.
It sounds like music.
Thrilled feels like spring.

Katie Reader
Age: 10

Salmon
tasty, brave
swimming, jumping, lying
It is very tasty.
Fish

Isaac Smith
Age: 9

I SAW A BEE AT THE SEA

I saw a bee at the sea,
he followed me home one day.
I came back and he was wearing a yellow coat.
He was at the sea coast,
he screamed when he saw me,
and I just giggled and said oh you silly bee.

Lauren Gillespie

FALL IS HERE

Red, yellow, green, and brown leaves
are changing colors all around.
Up and down all the streets,
leaves are falling off the trees.

Fall is here!

Sarah A. Veatch
Age: 7

BEST FRIENDS

Best friends since we were young,
We always had so much fun.
Even though we would push and shove,
When I was little I fell in love.
I guess I should have told you.
Maybe you would have loved me, too.
Now it's too late—it's either love or hate.
And now, years later,
You're with her—we're past tense,
We are were.

Kanishia Nichole Wilkinson

SNOW

Light and fluffy
snow is falling.
Fluttering to the ground,
light as a feather.

Snow on the branches.
Snow on the rooftops.
Snow everywhere!

Time for snowball fights!
Time to build Frosty the snowman.
Time to make snow angels.
Time for a mug of hot cocoa on a snowy day!

Maya A. Phan
Age: 7

THE RAIN'S PATH

The rain rattles on the red roof
Slipping, sliding, and splashing down the drain
As natural as the wind directs the weathervane
Each picking their own path
Every day a new decision—
Like me directing my own life
Choosing my course in college, career, and life

Kyle Cunningham
Age: 17

SUMMERTIME

Birds,
Bees,
Green leaves on trees,
And families in a swarm of fleas.
Families cry, "Help! Help,
Get these fleas away from me!"
Kids go down slides saying,
"Wheee, we like you in fleas.
When you get out of the fleas,
Please make us some macaroni and cheese."
My, my, look at the time,
I really must go,
So now all we gotta do is make sure,
The toilet doesn't overflow!

Katie Volz
Age: 7

HAPPINESS

Happiness is green.
It smells like fried eggs cooking.
It tastes like Fruit Loops crunching in my mouth.
It sounds like a kitty purring.
Happiness feels like playing tag with my friends.

Noah Guengerich
Age: 10

Teachers are fun.
They make me happy.
They always show up to school.
The teachers are always working,
No matter what!

Kerstan Troyer
Age: 8

Sunset, sunset,
How do you rise?
I like it when you rise.
I like your color.
It is beautiful.

Jayson Kolb
Age: 7

FALL TIME

Yellow leaves,
Orange leaves,
Harvesting fields,
Raking leaves,
Making big piles,
Bare trees,
And children having so much fun.

Collin Wacker
Age: 7

Paige
nice, sweet
caring, trusting, helping
She is my favorite.
Cousin

Payton Leichtenberg
Age: 9

A frog can jump really far.
Some frogs are hard to catch.
Some bullfrogs are mean.
The daddy is hard to catch.
Their legs can go really fast.

Jonathan Boland
Age: 7

FAMILIES

Families are good.
Families are nice.
You should be glad that you have a family.
Families take good care of you.
Your parents cook your food.
Doesn't it feel good to have a family?

Kayla Hoffman
Age: 7

Animal
hairy, silly
swinging, jumping, running
It is very crazy.
Monkey

Paige Hohner
Age: 9

Happiness is yellow.
It smells like apples.
It looks like summer in the air.
It tastes like apple pie being served everywhere.
It sounds like happy friends dancing while in the air.
Happiness feels like going to the park.

Cassandra Mundekis
Age: 9

Monkey
silly, crazy
climbing, jumping, running
like a dog fetching a bone
Exciting

Gavin Keefauver
Age: 9

LEAH

Baby sister with her tiny pink clothes,
sitting in her swing,
so happy, so content.

Curious brown eyes
searching for something to stare at,
everything is quiet when she doesn't cry.

Happy one minute,
sad the next,
time for a bottle.

Belly full, happy for now,
grab the camera.

Crying again,
change her diaper,
still crying,
grab the pacifier,
last resort,
turn on the vacuum.

Bundled up in blankets, so warm and toasty,
Staring up at me so trusting.
Rocking her in the chair my daddy rocked me in.

Finally she sleeps,
and the room is quiet again.
I look down and see
this peaceful little angel lying in my arms.

At last, sleep time means quiet time,
          TV time,
          me time.

Kelsey Jeter
Age: 14

BUTTERFLY

so pretty
flies so high
small colorful
flitter flitter flitter
in the sky

Taylor Webster
Age: 11

HORSES

Horses are fun
They like to run
An apple a day, keeps the doctor away
Oats and hay, keep hunger away
Carrots are a treat
Horses like to eat
Horses like to run
And play in the sun
Green grass is fun
For horses to eat and run
Beautiful horses are fun to see
They make me happy when they run free

Billie Jo Bute
Age: 9

MY SECRET

The lights are like stars
Floating in the sky.
The way I see it they sparkle.
I say look at the stars, they say it's just light.
The ceiling panels are like clouds floating in the sky.
They see ceiling panels, they don't see what I see.
I say use your imagination, they try and try.
They don't see.
I say it is my secret.

Jordan M. Estes
Age: 12

PIZZA

I love pizza very much
I have pizza for my lunch
I have pizza when I play
I have pizza every day

Dayana León-Araujo
Age: 10

SEA

Sea
beautiful, shiny
swimming, playing, carrying
I love the water.
Ocean

Brittany N. Clauss
Age: 9

KEVIN

Kevin is so weird
I think he might be growing a beard
He thinks he is such a joy
Kevin is a boy

Sammi Baier
Age: 9

HOT DOG

Hot dogs, hot dogs, they are the best,
They are better than all the rest.
One time I ate five hot dogs for a meal,
When I was done you can guess how I did feel.
Even though they gave me a stomachache that day,
Hot dogs are my favorite I still say.

Hannah Dunlap
Age: 9

TIMBER

I have a dog named Timber
We call him Timber Wimber
He likes to play with me all the time
Once he drank lemon-lime

Samantha A. Matthews
Age: 9

Football
fun, hard
tackle, kick, run
cool, mean, awesome, bad
Satisfying

Ben Bier
Age: 9

DROP OF A HAT

I was late to school on Monday
because a huge train was coming my way
I managed to dodge it
so you see my explanation is logic.

The teacher said, "Do you expect me to buy that,
I've heard some better stories
that have to do with a wildcat.
I'm going to have to call your dad.
He needs to know
you haven't been behaving good but bad."

I yelled, "No don't do that."
She took out her cell phone
in the tip of a hat.
So I decided to be truthful
By the time I finish I won't be youthful.

I said, "Okay here is the truth
I got stuck in a kissing booth,
playing around with my friends."
Everyone laughed the teacher said,
"It never ends!"

She looked at me with a smile,
I just stood there for a while.
I said, "Did you really buy that?"
She took out her cell phone
in a drop of a hat.

Jackie Johnson
Age: 11

BIKES FLY HIGH IN THE SKY

Bikes fly high in the sky, they ride around in the sky.
Sometimes they come crashing down!
But you have to get up and do it again.
Sometimes you have to try,
the bigger jumps way in the sky.
The faster you go, the higher you fly!

Levi Ulysses King
Age: 12

B aseball is fun
A t the park
T o do in summer with your friends

Donavan Mundekis
Age: 9

THE BIG BAD FIGHT

I went to the Festival of Lights.
There ended up being a big fight!
Then the man needed to stop.
Thus he got stopped by the cops.

Then the man went to jail.
And his plan was a fail.
He had gone to a creepy cell.
And he had started to yell.

Then the man began to break out!
Then the cops began to pout.
Which was parked by a bar.

Then he drove to New York.
Where he tried to eat with a fork.
Then he tried a very good dish.
Which was a plate full of fish.

Then the man started to gamble.
He had won and started to ramble.
Then the man was chased by the cops.
Just for stealing some really nice props.

Now the man was on the run!
And he wasn't having much fun.
Then the cops caught up to him.
Then they threw him in a bin.

Now they strapped him in a bed.
Now they know his name is Jed.
Now they know why he was mad.
Just because his son had been bad.

Now everything was worked out.
And everyone began to shout.
He found out that he had been dumb.
And he got to see his son.

Now they all had to stay.
Just for one more really bad day.
Now they get to go home.
Which they live in a giant dome.

Now that they're at their giant house.
They realize that they have a mouse.
Now they keep her and call her Deb.
Which she sleeps in a really big bed.

Eric Douglas DeMattia
Age: 12

TIME TO RHYME

Gold is so shiny,
Toddlers are so whiney.
I know a mime,
Who wishes he could rhyme.

David Alan Tuley
Age: 11

WINTER FUN

My favorite time of year is winter
Because of all the snow that falls.
We also get to drink hot chocolate
With the mini marshmallows.

We also love to ride on sleds
After we get out of bed.
We also have snowball fights
Then we turn on the Christmas lights.

After we turn on the lights
We go to bed before Santa's big flight.
We hope to see presents under the tree
And if there are we'll shout with glee!

Brittany Amm
Age: 11

IN FALL

I like to play football.
I like it so much
But I always munch.
Caramel apples are so good
I stuff them in my hood.
I eat turkey.
He's a little perky.

Jacob Scott Pennington
Age: 9

CHRISTMAS LIGHTS

Every Christmas my family
we work together and trim our tree
our Christmas lights shine so bright
in the dark on Christmas night

They shimmer and shine
all in a line
always in sight
all morning and night

They bring so much cheer
every year
the mistletoe and the snow
are not as good as lights that glow

Taylor Marie Araujo
Age: 11

PUTTING SADIE TO SLEEP

I love to put Sadie to sleep.
When you put Sadie to sleep,
You need her blanket and her tail.
She likes to bite her tail,
And have her blanket over her.
She is, yes, a cat . . .
But a very good cat!

Allison Bline
Age: 8

I HATE TEARS

I hate the tears
Caused by peers
The people who cry
Might feel they could die

So don't tease
And I won't say please
Because they might not achieve
'Cause they did not believe

So if you don't like to cry
And don't want to die
Be nice to other peers so they would believe
That they can achieve!!!

Jacqueline Struebing
Age: 11

SUMMER

Summer is the best season.
I will give a good reason.
We have no school,
And that's really cool.
That's why I love this season.

Andrew Zigtema
Age: 11

CHRISTMASTIME

Christmas is coming
The time my mom fears
Sledding and snowball fights
To children it brings cheers

Snow on the ground
Lots of presents being found
Putting up the trees
Presents cost many fees

The presents bring many joys
Some get the flu
Enjoying all the toys
Angel on the tree so true

Mercedes Thurston
Age: 12

CHARMED IS COOL

CHARMED is my favorite TV show.
My grandma says it's a big no no.
The witchcraft makes it so fun,
There are no church nuns.
When I watch CHARMED I say whoa.

Natasha A. Swanberg
Age: 11

THE BEST TIME OF YEAR IS CHRISTMAS

Christmas is the best,
There's not any time to rest,
Because you have to hang up lights,
The whole block is bright.

There is a lot of snow,
All boys and girls know,
Christmas brings St. Nick,
You can never see his trick.

There is always snow on the ground,
There is always the joyous sound,
Of carolers singing,
And sleigh bells ringing.

Christmas colors of red and green,
Are the most beautiful I've seen,
They reflect off the snow,
To make a lovely light show.

At first light of day,
You could hear him say,
Ho! Ho! Ho!
Now it's Christmas you know.

Melisa Trout
Age: 11

CHRISTMAS IS THE BEST TIME OF THE YEAR

Everyone is full of happy cheer,
We are all out of school until next year.
We all hope to receive presents,
We may have to eat pheasant.
Santa Claus arrives by his reindeer.

The snow falls from the sky,
Be careful or it will fly in your eye.
Christmas is for reaching out,
Christmas is what love's about.
So enjoy this special time before it flies by.

Jamie Sue Gadberry
Age: 12

THE GREAT SUMMER

Summer is fun.
Summer is hot.
You can play in the sun
A lot.

You don't need to go to school.
Instead you can swim in a pool.
It will be a bummer.
At the end of summer.

Satya Yerrabolu
Age: 11

CHRISTMASTIME

When Christmastime comes around,
All the kids clown around,
Parents want to skip this time of year,
Instead they give a holiday cheer,

Christmas trees are so tall,
Little ornaments so so small,
Mistletoe hung real high,
Santa's sleigh up in the sky,

Little kids tucked up tight,
Trying not to stay up all night,
Little kids please don't fight,
'Cause Santa Claus comes tonight.

Sheyann Rosemary Williams
Age: 12

Jarrett
Athletic, brave, popular
Son of Jenny and Flint Greer and Justin Dean
Brother of Julia, Jake, and Jeremy
Loves sports, animals, Ohio State
Fears school, clowns, haircuts
Wants to see SANTA CLAUSE 3,
Ohio State football game
Lives in Manito, Illinois
Dean

Jarrett Dean
Age: 9

LOVE YOU FOREVER

My mom said she would love me forever
She could never
Not love me
Even if I was one of three

I love my mom
And she loves me
Even if I was a boy named Tom
With a pet flea

We might get in fights
Because of my attitude
We argue day and night
What a terrible feud

Love you forever
I could never
Not love you
There's my clue

From me to you
I love you
And you love me
Can't you see

Love You Forever

Emily Roberts
Age: 11

Football
rough, easy
rushing, blocking, kicking
quarterback, running back, ball, basket
shooting, running, dribbling
fun, fast-paced
Basketball

Marshall John Shimmin
Age: 9

PRAY FOR PEACE

Christmastime is near,
A holiday, to many, that is very dear.
Everyone eager to decorate the tree,
Taking for granted that we are free.
So many rushing to the store,
Each year spending even more.
It is not how big the toy,
It is being with family and full of joy.
Remember those who are alone,
Fighting for freedom and chilled to the bone.
Be grateful that you are you,
Think about what you can do.
Pray for peace and more,
Ask God to end this bloody war.

Taylor Harty
Age: 11

Tabitha
funny, kind
helping, protecting, caring
Tabby is very fun.
Friend

Brianna N. Morrison
Age: 9

IF I WERE A BIRD

If I were a bird, I would fly up high into the sky.
If I were hungry, I would land on a bush
and eat up all the berries.
If I were tired, I would fly to a tree
and would go to my nest and sleep.
In the morning, I would fly up high
and sing my morning song.
Soon it will be time to lay eggs
and wait for my babies to hatch.
I would teach my baby birds
to sing beautiful morning songs
and fly up really high into the sky.
But now it's time to go to sleep and be me again.
Tomorrow, I will pretend to be a butterfly.
It's been a busy day.

Yilan Yang
Age: 8

Dog
loving, playful
digging, running, sleeping
black Lab, miniature pinscher, Siamese, tabby
playing, purring, scratching
funny, silly
Cat

Tamera Henderson
Age: 8

Alexis
Funny, pretty, loud
Daughter of Autumn and Jeff
Sister of Abbie and Nathan
Loves tacos, Mom, Dad
Fears sharks, jellyfish, Mrs. Berg
Wants to see Grand Canyon, octopi
Lives in Manito, Illinois
Martin

Alexis Martin
Age: 9

MARTIN'S ROUGH DAY

When Martin was little he came home from school
And he had a very rough day
So he went to his friend's house
And asked their mom if they could play
Their mother said, "No, now please go away"

Martin went home and said,
"Mother what's going on today?"
His mother told him about segregation
Martin asked, "Does that mean separation?"
His mother said, "Yes"
Martin said, "That's a mess"
Martin said, "That's not fair"
While his mother kissed him in the hair

When Martin was older
He got more bolder
And he led a crowd
They howled and howled
'Til they got what they wanted

Keyonna Perry-Edwards
Age: 10

Birthdays
Cake, candles
We get presents
Have lots of fun

Tom Brya
Age: 7

Memories
feel good
make me smile
not always nice though
some are scary
many fun
Memories

Caroline Gillette
Age: 8

Sharks
sharp teeth
love meaty things
love to bite everything
big fat mouths
good hunters
Sharks

Liam Daly
Age: 7

Ice cream
Chocolate, vanilla
Cold and sugary
Tastes creamy and good

Kevin Hinders
Age: 7

TURKEY

Turkey jerky is so sweet
I love to eat it on the street
Turkey lurkey is so fine
I love to eat it all the time

Kenzie Carwyle
Age: 12

THE JUNGLE

The jungle is a wonderful place!
The jungle is a place where you can roam free,
and there's a lot of fruit you can eat.
There are joyful animals
like monkeys, lizards, and giraffes.
There are a lot of dangerous animals, too.
The dangerous animals are lions, tigers, and bears.
The jungle is a wild place where you can roam free!

Jake Pankey
Age: 10

I see pumpkin decorations
I hear scary Halloween noises
I smell warm pumpkin bread
I feel the hot candles burning
I taste my yummy candy
Fall is here! I love it!

Ian Wallace
Age: 7

Sharks
Mean, furious
Dangerous, bad things
They are meat-eaters.

Tommy Krouse
Age: 8

S harp nose
W onderful
O ver-powerful
R ough
D angerous
F ish
I ncredible
S cary
H urtful

Taggart VanEtten
Age: 11

Brownies
yummy, good
sweet and tasty
taste wonderful with milk
excellent after school
favorite treat
Brownies

Claire Cowser
Age: 8

Saints
Heavenly people
God chose them.
They live in Heaven.
Love us all
Help poor
Saints

Anwyn Payonk
Age: 8

Pumpkins
orange, roundish
carving, picking, painting
Pumpkin pie is good.
Jack-o'-lantern

Abby Farrell

Maggie
Cute, fast
Loves us a lot
Likes running in fields

Max Cochrane
Age: 8

Birthday
getting presents
eating delicious cake
celebrating eight years old
playing party games
inviting friends
Birthday

Meagan Borgsmiller
Age: 7

I love bugs!
Red bugs,
Green bugs,
Even orange and creepy bugs.
I love that they glow.
I love when they sing.
I love that they hop all around.
I love bugs!

Madison Crawford
Age: 8

God
Nice, fun
Loves and cares
King of the world

Grace Hansen
Age: 7

School
It rocks
Fun and exciting
It is the greatest.

Kevin Dwyer
Age: 7

PICKLEY

I bought a pickle
It cost one nickel
It was sour
So I put my tongue under the shower

I took another bite
I tried not to scream
It was not a lovely sight
My eyes were agleam

Harley Garlinger
Age: 11

Flowers
Red, pink
Graceful and beautiful
The ground is full.

Meredith Jackson
Age: 8

Horses
Brown, black
Very big animals
Much fun to ride

Nellie Grace Haug
Age: 8

CHRISTMAS IS SO WONDERFUL

Christmas is a wonderful time of year
because there's magical flying reindeer
and Santa who's jolly all day
with his nine reindeer that eat hay.

Santa brings lots of presents
on top his big red sleigh
down the chimney he goes
so all the children can play.

Aaron Jensen
Age: 11

Church
God's house
It is peaceful
Place where people pray.

Avery Oldfield
Age: 7

Dance
Jazz, hip-hop
Ballet, tap, lyrical
Dance is very fun.

Sophie Leskis
Age: 7

TORTELLINI

My favorite food is tortellini.
It's yummy and saucy.
Good with cheese,
It's meaty inside.
It's Italian pasta (maybe Mexican)
It's good with peaches to me.
It's big and round.
And it's red.
The best sauce with it to me is Prego sauce.

Matthew English
Age: 9

WHERE AM I

I am here, I am there,
Sometimes it seems like I'm everywhere.
You see me here, you see me there,
But do you really care?
You may, you also may not,
But that goes to show, you don't see me a lot.
I will come, I will go,
I am high, I am low.
I stop, I go,
I'm fast, I'm slow,
I say yes, and I also say no.
Where am I, who am I,
I am unknown to every single guy.
I must go, I will not come,
And I will be missed, only by some.
Good-bye, and farewell,
I will never return, for I must not say.

Shelby A. Hulse
Age: 13

Sharks
Blue, gray
Gills to breathe
Teeth to eat fish.

Edward Warinner
Age: 7

Praise be to the King.
Precious are His promises.
On the cross He died.

Cody Tybroski
Age: 9

Christmas
snowy winter
jingle bells ring
Santa visits good children.
wonderful family fun
Jesus' birthday
Christmas

Riley Knight
Age: 7

I love bugs!
Jumping bugs,
Lightning bugs,
Even yellow and orange bugs.
I love when they glow.
I love when they suck.
I love that they are creepy.
I love bugs!

Drew Dobbins
Age: 7

Halloween
scary, spooky
scaring, wearing, tearing
Kids are trick-or-treating.
October

Nate Guido
Age: 8

God is our Savior.
We love God and He loves us.
God gave me a dog.

Maddisen Miner
Age: 8

LOVE

Love is here and there!
Love is everywhere.
Love is up.
Love is down.
Love is your soul.
Love is what makes us glow.
Love is what we need.
Just in case you did not know.

Asia Faulkner
Age: 10

BALL GAME

People shouting!
Drums sounding off in joyful glee!
Players running down the court, shouting happily!
Candy, soda, popcorn!!!
The smell, it overcomes me!!
The band is playing!
Music that seems to spark,
To spark life!!
Sitting with friends,
Time to share our dreams and cheer our teams!
Fingers painted red and white;
Oh this everlasting night!!!
The school song rings out,
This victory is yet announced!!
The second game starts, exciting and fun!
The band plays out one last time,
Even though the game's only begun.
People clap and shout out loud!
The crowd, it grows so large!!
The buzzer sounds for halftime,
Our team is winning!
Here they come again!
Ten more seconds on the clock,
Victory is ours again!!!

Erica L. Sheeran
Age: 13

TRAINS

T ime doesn't fly when you're on a train . . .
R eading for one hour . . .
A rrows point to where I have to go . . .
 I mpassioned, I walked between the cars . . .
N ight is falling, I'm still in the train . . .
S oftly over the mountains, I fall asleep.

Ishani D. Trzaska
Age: 8

God is our Father.
His love endures forever.
I love the Lord God.

Ethan Loew
Age: 10

THE DAY THE WORLD HAD CHANGED

From now until the very end
Many cannot ever mend
The day we will not ever forget
When the Twin Towers were hit
The tragic day on the 11th of September
That we will always remember
Many have been injured or lost their lives
They were people's children, husbands, and wives
Either from the Pentagon, planes, or towers
All happened within a matter of hours
And to all firefighters and policeman for doing their best
Because on that day, all their skills were put to the test
Rescuing people and saving lives is what they had to do
Even though they didn't know
What they were heading into
And to all those heroes on that day
Even those who helped in the smallest way
Five years later, the truth still remained
This is the day the world had changed

Danielle Carroll
Age: 18

FOREST BEAUTY

Plants and animals
What does the forest behold?
Defining beauty

Drennen Kessinger
Age: 10

SANTA

Santa is the greatest.
Santa is good at giving people presents.
Santa's elves make good toys for girls and boys.

Genia Gray
Age: 7

GOD

God is the gift of love.
He prays for us.
He can be your father if you don't have one.
God can help you.

Jordan Hall-Streater
Age: 7

THANKSGIVING

I am thankful for my parents, turkey,
my dogs, Spirit and Sassy.
I am thankful for Genia, Jimmy, Breanna, and Sissy.
I am thankful for my toys.

Heather Zelechowski
Age: 8

Football
fun, game
hard, run, catching
hot, warm, cool, rough
Sport

Dylan McCanless
Age: 8

Ballet
fun dancing
makes me happy
fun, kid's thing, cool
Dancing

Alyssa Evans
Age: 7

SEASONS BLOOM

The seasons change in different ways.
Spring has new babies born.
Winter is snowballs with fun.
Fall there are piles of leaves full of happiness.
Summer is the time to relax with sleepiness.

Allyssa Agne
Age: 7

FISHING

It's fun fishing.
You can relax.
My dad takes me on the boat when we fish.
Sometimes my dad catches really big fish.
Sometimes I catch big fish.

Sadie Dillard
Age: 7

I AM ON THE STAGE

I'm up on the stage
The spotlight on me
What should I do?
Should I laugh?
Should I run away?

The music starts
My feet start to move.

I keep on dancing
My smile so big
I love to dance
It is my life's dream!

Emma Cooper
Age: 9

MY DOG WINSTON

Winston sits for a bone.
He's a great dog most of the time.
He gets into the trash.
Bad dog!
Winston puts his little paws on me.
He sits on my stomach.
He thinks he's cool all the time.
Winston wears my sunglasses.

Nicholas Reynolds Hahn
Age: 8

WORMS

My worm is neat.
He doesn't eat meat.
He's very very long.
And he can sing you a song.

Ashlei Taylor
Age: 9

OCEAN WHISPER

Listen
Beauty
Can you hear it talking?
It whispers, do you hear it now?
I do

Claire Corpus
Age: 10

OCTOBER

October is the season of colorful leaves
The season of long sleeves
Everything is fun
Thinking of fall is fun for everyone

Jordan Beckman
Age: 10

Car
fast, big
takes people places
makes me feel cool
Machine

Dylan McGhee
Age: 8

MY WORM IS CRAZY!

My worm is blue.
His name is Crew.
He likes water.
But he's not a crawler!

Melanie Hutchins
Age: 9

WORMS

Red wigglers like to wiggle,
And red wigglers like to giggle,
Red wigglers are red,
And the one I have is named Ed.

Breann Sandage
Age: 9

FALL

October is fun, fun to everyone.
We like to jump in leaves
that fall slowly to the ground.
We pile them up in a very big mound.
We pile them up and then we jump.
I love to play outside in fall.
Who would not like fall at all?
Fall is fun, fun to everyone.
I want to give God praise,
even on the coldest days.

Canaan Beckman
Age: 10

A WORM NAMED GRACE

There once was a worm named Grace.
  She loved to wear lace.
    She doesn't use a rake.
      She loves funnel cake.

She once ate lead.
  She was almost dead.
    Thanks to Doctor Kline,
      She's just fine.

Sadie Bronnbauer
Age: 9

Jets
Fast, loud
They help us
They are very cool
BF2 bomber

Rhett Romanik
Age: 8

FRIENDS

Make new friends.
If you don't have any,
You can make some.
Friends are fun.
You can share with them.
Friends sit by you at lunch.
They play with you at recess.

Olivia Johnson
Age: 8

BROOK OF LIFE

As the small brook trickles past stone and pebbles
the frogs croak and swim freely
as their tadpoles swim around
happily waiting for their legs.
In the distance you see a deer
drinking from the brook
as always aware of its surroundings.
As the sun starts to set
all the animals tucker down
for a good night's rest
as the raccoon just starts to wake up
for a meal of crawdads.
The owl flies overhead like a fighter jet
on a mission after the mouse
for his meal of the night.
The mouse runs away but this does no good
the owl catches.
As the owl and the raccoon
and all the other animals of the night
go to sleep for their day's rest,
the sun comes back up yawns and stretches its arms
as it shines its light back on the brook.
This is the brook of life.

Nick J. Ammann
Age: 14

DEFEAT

Eckstein up to bat
and Rogers rubs his hat
Rolen takes a lead
while Rogers chooses speed

Eckstein hits a single
in our spine we feel a tingle
Rogers throws but makes an error
Tigers' fans fill with terror

If Pujols uses his might
we're sure to win this fight

Clare Amann
Age: 12

MY WORM!

My worm's name is Ed.
He likes to be fed.
He is brown.
And he acts like a clown.
He loves to eat green leaves.
He cannot get fleas.
He likes to run.
But he doesn't like the sun.
Ed has no eyes.

Gage Carlson
Age: 9

JAY

It was the middle of the night,
I heard my mom's voice filled with fright.

I heard a voice say "It's pretty bad."
The voice on the phone
was my best friend's dad.

Her uncle, a policeman, was working late.
He never would have guessed his fate.

A broken neck, two legs in casts.
They didn't know how long he'd last.

We got the call, I started to cry.
I cried more and more.
I thought the tears would never cease to pour.
I felt scared, my friend alone.
I know he went to a better place,
but I yearn every day to see his face.

Darby Christopher
Age: 12

LET'S BE GOOD, THAT'S ALL

"You're good, but not great.
That's a seven, can I see an eight?"

I know, I know. It's all so defeating, and I am alone.
Everyone . . . EVERYWHERE. They glance away,
not even an awkward stare.
Just once, I plead. But to no avail.
Even in friends and in those dear—
I find no appeal to how I feel.

In the inner city—there's a wake-up call.
Ring, Ring. It's reality in your face!
Shove aside: geometry, psychology, anthropology—
because right here you'll find
    The deepest pain and hurt to ever put on a shirt.
    It's in his face and on his clothes,
    nothing more than what it shows.
You'll see, and sentimental you will be—
but will you touch? Will you allow a smudge?
On your good deeds and on your brand-new hoodies.

You see this hurt—it won't go away—it's here to stay.
But reality is cool in that it will change, if you're no fool.
If you love this hurt in his shirt, if you hug this pain,
without wanting gain.
I guarantee you will see how it works.
    When you give what you want—
    and then what you want, is only to give.

So I'm here at home writing this poem.
Good, not great—maybe a seven, but not an eight.
And to those who put me down, I will give no frown.
And my friends and those dear—
with them I might even shed a tear.
Because I remember the hurt, I remember his name.
So for me to want glory would be a tragic shame.
Those wake-up calls are what reveal light—
into what really matters and what should be in sight.
  So I will give what I want, and then want only to give.
  Truly, this is to live.

Caleb A. Butler
Age: 15

SNOW

The snow is white
It's so, so bright
It shines like the sun 'til night has begun
It melts away until the day has gone away
So today is the last day of winter

Hannah Kaiser
Age: 9

MY FRIEND

There was a girl who likes to shop
She buys a lot of purses
She has a profession
That profession is a nurse
She likes to hang out with friends
She talks to them at school
She likes to have friends over
When they are over they act like fools

She has brown hair
She has braces
She has brown eyes
She wears Shox with white laces
She lives in New Baden
Her house is near county line
The house she lives in is a two-story home
Her house is very fine

Jessica Eversgerd
Age: 12

CASSIE

I have a best friend
Her name is Cassie
She really likes to laugh
And sometimes she can be sassy

She is one of three girls
Who are all very funny
They like to go swim
When the days are sunny

Although they are close
They still tend to fight
Sometimes in the day
But mostly at night

Even though they do fight
They still love each other
Because they have good personalities
Just like their mother

Morgan Fochtmann
Age: 12

There once was a girl named Bell
She found a pretty shell
It was on the ground
It was big and round
So she took it to show and tell

Mikayla Hill
Age: 12

My grandma is really nice
She lives two hours away
She likes to be with her grandchildren
Sometimes we go there to stay

She likes to garden
She likes to farm
She likes to quilt
She owns a barn

She lives next to her sister
She lives in Mount Carmel
We love to talk to her
We will talk to her tomorrow

She likes to shop
She has had a few tears
She's the oldest of five
She has been married forty plus years

Megan Frerking
Age: 12

PATRICK STUMP

He is my favorite singer
He says quiet is the new loud
He looks like a teddy bear, cute and plump
These traits make him proud

He's short and Irish
He used to play the drums
The only thing you will hear from him
Is his voice not his hums

He is in the band Fall Out Boy
He has beautiful green eyes
He likes to be himself
He always aims for the prize
He is from a Chicago suburb,
A nice little town
He's too sweet to be mean
So his fame won't bring him down

Courtney Egner
Age: 12

Pups
very small
make you happy
make me feel good
Cute

Gabby Hancher
Age: 8

A LIFE'S TRUE BLESSINGS

Even in the dismal times
Things can turn around
I finally start to open my eyes
To things that I have found

In the midst of hardship
Your self-respect may fall
No matter who tries to help
They never really helped at all

Yet as everyone keeps persisting
Showing me how much I am loved
I learned that in reality
At least I am not being pushed and shoved

Looking back at me I see
The pleasures that fill my days
This part of my life turned around
Like a fairy-tale story in many ways

I know while my life changes
I lost friends and so much more
But everything that is up must come down
And I hope to open another new door

Throughout a teenager's life
And the places that they go
People learn from the mistakes they make
And just simply go with the flow

Count your blessings every night
To know your life is worth living
People may constantly come and go
But some never stop giving

Even in the worst of times
Your true friends will always be there
So never give up or back down
Because they always truly care

Kristen Wehmeyer
Age: 15

BONDING WITH A FRIEND

Riding through the trees
Feeling the nice cool breeze
Bonding with a friend
As memories flood back again
Riding along with ease
Hearing the rustle of trees
Enjoying the company of a friend
Whose love is mine again
I know this time won't last
And will soon become the past
But for now we ride as one
Enjoying a bright warm sun
Tomorrow is a different day
One hundred years away

Alyssa Forsyth
Age: 12

MIKAYLA HILL

She has blue eyes
also blonde hair
She is really nice
and she cares

She has three sisters and one brother
She plays basketball, soccer,
and she loves
to play volleyball

She has a weird laugh
it is very funny
She also has a pet parrot
now she wants a bunny

She moved here from Minnesota
and she loves her little sis
Her stepdad's name is Marty
can you guess who it is?

Hannah Kolmer
Age: 12

ELLIE

There was a little old woman
who was oh so sweet
She loved to watch children make snowmen
and watch them compete.

She always longed to watch and learn
always remembering special days
She lived nice and long
and always was amazed

She looked like an angel
who was beautiful,
smart, and funny,
and oh so sweet.

She was born in 1911
her complexions were a very good mix
She now is in Heaven
She died in 2006.

Elexus Lohman
Age: 12

LASSIE

She was a dog
She lived long
We took her in
She lived a happy life
She has new friends
She had a place in our family
She was nice to cats and dogs
We loved her
She knew tricks
She liked to be scratched on her tummy
She was very kind
She died in the yard
She was helpful
She still lives in our hearts

Joshua Reuss
Age: 13

MY BEST FRIEND

Dad
fun, caring
mowing, playing, talking
my very best friend
A friend

Brennen Little
Age: 12

HANNAH KOLMER

This girl's name is Hannah
Hannah's my best friend
We've known each other since we were four
Our friendship will never end

Hannah is smart
She is also kind
She has a lot of friends
Sometimes can't make up her mind

If Hannah should get hurt
I know that I would cry
We'll always stick together
I hope we never die

For someone born with brown hair and blue eyes
I know we'll always have fun
Even if she goes away
I'll still see her in the sun

Rachael Conley
Age: 12

RECCURRING DREAM

Deep sleeping, tucked in tight
please don't let me have the same dream tonight
Where I am being chased
and I run out of breath
Where I'm trying to escape
and find my way home
I run and roam
but never reach my destination
Being back home would be a sensation
Oh no! They're back!
Watch out for their brutal attack!
Finally, I wake, drenched in a sweat
this dream will come back to haunt me, I bet

Lillian Nicole Hurley
Age: 12

DANCING

Dancing is my favorite thing to do.
It is so much fun.
It gives me energy.
It keeps me moving.
You can make your own dance moves.
You can do what you want to do.
You can buy a hip-hop dance tape.

Tanisha Luster
Age: 8

SNOW

Oh snow!
Snow is white
Snow is a snowball
Snow is a snowman
Snow is a snowflake.

I like to play in the snow
I like to make an angel in the snow.

Oh snow!
I love the snow
But the best thing about snow
Is there is no school!

Chyanne Finnegan
Age: 9

VOLLEYBALL

Volleyball isn't it fun?
Volleyball you gotta be tall
Volleyball you play in the sun.

Volleyball you gotta hit the ball
WAIT do you want to fall?
Volleyball, oh volleyball!
How I love it all!

Gracyn Norsigian
Age: 9

MIGHTY PUJOLS

When he came to bat
That very day
He was due to score
This was a time to pay

He looked at the ball
Ready to bat
The crowd went quiet
Like straw on a hat

The pitcher threw the ball
And there was a boo
The ump said, "Strike 1"
As the batter went "Ptooo"

It came to the last one
As noise went 'bout
But everyone left
Because Mighty Pujols struck out

Sean Cox
Age: 12

TWEETY

Tweety my bird was very mean
She kept herself very clean
She pecked us oh so hard
Even though her cage was barred
Sometimes she sat on my arm
But she caused me a lot of harm

Tweety was very tough
She played very rough
She knew how to open the door
And climb all the way to the floor
We had her for two years
Her beak was like two spears
She loved to go outside
But out there she died

Hannah Schlarman
Age: 10

Lava lamp
bright, retro
sinking, rising, glowing
going up and down
My night-light

Seth Powers
Age: 13

BIBLE

Wanting to save people's lives
Before they take a nosedive
Saving my heart
So I can start
A new way to thrive

Danica M. García
Age: 12

CHRISTMAS DAY!

Yeah! It's Christmas Day!
Let's say hooray for this holiday.
The winter snow, the winter breeze,
I can't wait to put up the tree!
The bells to the stockings so much to see,
And maybe if you are quiet,
You could see Santa come down your chimney!

Kayla Wood
Age: 9

PEYTON MANNING

He played football at Tennessee.
Weighing two hundred thirty pounds,
is Peyton Manning.
Yelling to his receivers, making loud sounds.

Peyton is my favorite football player,
because he does good deeds.
He helped people from Hurricane Katrina,
especially the ones with major needs.

He stands six feet, five inches,
and wears Number 18.
Peyton plays quarterback for the Colts,
and could be the best you've ever seen.

He has a brother that plays too,
but for the New York Giants,
They get along every once in a while,
but would never form an alliance.

Cory Arentsen
Age: 12

I have a friend, yes a best friend.
He helps me keep cool in the summer,
my heart he can mend.
I love him, he decorates my yard in the fall.
His beauty is gone in the winter, but he is very tall.
I will always love him, my best friend.

Emily Culler
Age: 12

The person I write about I know well
He is my dad
A man beyond compare
And like no fad

A helper to all
He coaches teams with profession
For he worked hard as a teen to fulfill his dream
He manages to win games without any expression

In free time he enjoys to hunt
He helps me to succeed by putting me before himself
In his experiences he has learned a lot
Without his help and tips
I may have ended up hurting myself

My father has taught me well
Without him I might be a lost soul
For without a cause in life
You might as well bury yourself in a hole

Justin Groennert

MY BEST FRIEND

I know a brunette
Who acts like a blonde
She is very smart
And of her boyfriend is very fond

She loves to watch TV
She plays bass clarinet
She has a dog named Cuddles
Who is her favorite pet

She's very sweet
She's very short
She loves her cats
And she loves sports

She's very nice
She's my best friend
And what's really sad
Is that this poem has come to an end

Caitlin Johnson
Age: 12

TIMELESS

I climb uphill from our car
And make my way
To the top of the mountain.

The clouds seem to magically pass through the trees
On an overcast day four thousand feet up.
I climb the spiral ramp to the observation tower.

After the long climb, I look out.
I can't see very far,
But I feel like something mystic
Is on this mountain.
There are other people here, but I feel alone,

Like part of the mountain.

Will Rieger
Age: 12

ISLAND

mountainous region
waves crashing to the white sand
crushing shells below

Chris Isenhower
Age: 12

Lauren Dowdy
nice and sensitive
caring, understanding, and shopping
She's my best friend.
Dowdy

Cristina White
Age: 13

SKY

Enchanted white clouds
Blue like the Caribbean
Peaceful as the woods

Matthew Schaeffer
Age: 12

OUR UNITED STATES OF AMERICA

United States
large, loud
voting, talking, living
Wonderful place to live.
Part of the world

Lauren Haukapp
Age: 12

THE SUN

My mom said the sun goes up,
Then it goes down.
With a beautiful shine,
Like the pretty shine of
    You and me.

Blain Faught
Age: 8

Cardinals
athletic, awesome
winning, pitching, hitting
won the World Series
Redbirds

Jared M. Kues
Age: 12

DAD

Courage
exciting, great
hunting, fishing, building
one of a kind
Dad

Colin Vahlkamp
Age: 13

WAITING ROOMS

Always sitting in waiting rooms
With a sad look in my eyes
Playing with my sick Barbie dolls
While helping to waste the time
Hoping that my mother would come out alive

As I'm getting older, walking up the basement stairs
Deciding what it is that I shall be
I want to help the suffering people
Bless many families' hearts
As the doctor that saved my mother

As I just saved the life
Of an innocent young man
I watch over him
As he hardly lives
After days, weeks, and months go by
He wakes for the first time
Lying in a stiff hospital bed
With an unusual look in his eyes
All better now, he thanks me
For saving his life

Stefani Waldhaus
Age: 15

ALPHABET BACKPACK

A wesome
B ook-carrier
C arry it every day
D rop it on floors
E asy to carry on shoulders
F olders inside
G obs of stuff
H eavy at times
 I like it
 J unk-carrier
K eeps my books from getting lost
L ug it around
M essy
N ot easy to keep clean
O rganizes me
P ockets everywhere
Q uick to pack
R am it full
S traps
T ravels with me everywhere
U seful
V ery handy
W heels on some
X tra cool
Y our kind of style
Z ippers all over

Paige Marshall
Age: 8

CELEBRATE!!!

I really like the month of May
because it has a special day.
It's on May 5—
It feels like a gift.
All the presents I see
are all wrapped up for me.
Mom bakes a pretty cake.
Pictures of smiles are what Dad must take.
I blow out the candles on this day.
It's my favorite because:
It's my birthday!!!

Aleetha Mulch
Age: 9

DUSTIN

D ad's littlest boy.
U nloads lots of pigs.
S upports my dad's farm.
T ractors are my favorite equipment.
I nquisitive all the time.
N othing better than being a farmer.

Dustin, that's me!

Dustin Speckhart
Age: 8

FALL

During the fall I watch leaves fall off trees
They flow through the air with such ease
I watch creatures come into my yard for food
Then can't find any and have a mood
I like to feel the breeze
As it goes through my hair like a cool sneeze

I can't get enough of fall
And watch the wind blow trees that are tall
I like to play in the leaves
But they sometimes make me sneeze

Deer-hunting season
Is one of my reasons to love this season
I never can say I don't love this time of year
But I can say this is my time to be cheer

Leah M. Dallmier
Age: 14

MY CAT

My cat
Lies down
In my bed
Every night
Because I let him.

Codi Mast
Age: 8

NEW YEAR'S EVE

Some have parties
With their friends
Time with family
That never ends
All to count down
The seconds left
'Til the new year's birth
And the old year's death
Resolutions will be made
To better one's self
Memories are remembered
Then left on the shelf
Now our ages are growing
As another year goes by
Remember to enjoy the moment
For the time does fly

Makenzie Marie Weishaar
Age: 14

G rilling
R ibs
A lways watching
N ever stopping
D oing the thing he loves
P assionately
A lways missing you

Connor Anthony Kabbes
Age: 8

TRICK-OR-TREAT

T rick-or-treat
R ed fireballs
 I nch by inch candy goes by.
Candy and prizes
K acie and me go together

O pen candy wrappers on the ground
R ed lollipops

T hey give out lots of candy
R yan and me go together
E ven lots of gum
A t trick-or-treat it's fun
T rick-or-treat

Meranda Shaw
Age: 11

NEVER MIND THE RAIN OR SNOW!

Never mind the rain, never mind the snow!
For the rain doesn't leave a stain,
and for the snow melts before you know.

But if rain and snow were to be together,
That would be pretty nasty weather!

Isabella Gardner
Age: 10

B ounce pass
A wesome
S portsmanship
K nowledge
E nergetic
T eam
B ackboard
A ctive
L ay-up
L oyalty

Kacie Hilt
Age: 10

Moms are beautiful.
They can be angry or nice.
My mom is all these.

Deanna Helmuth
Age: 10

MOTHER

Careful, helpful
Loves to play
Nice, friendly, and fun
Loving forever and my maker

Damion Shumard
Age: 10

AMERICA

A ll are free
M y country
E veryone together
R aising the flag
I nspired to be safer
C itizens coming together
A ll for freedom

Luke B. Jansen
Age: 11

VC

Vince Carter is on fire
he's the best high flyer
he dunked over Ming
because he is the king
and he facialed Shaq
around his back
he plays for the Nets
and cheering is what he gets
he can shoot and spin
so the Nets always win

Carter Wills
Age: 10

HALLOWEEN

H ow crazy is
A lot of candy
L ots of scaring
L ots of toilet-papering
O h how the ghosts go boo
W e have lots of fun
E ven trick-or-treat nights
E ven haunted houses
N ighttime is when you go trick-or-treating

Kortney Doty
Age: 10

ONCE I MADE A PUMPKIN PIE

Once I made a pumpkin pie
that could fly. Oh my!
When it flew it said boo!
So what did I do?
I did the same thing of course,
I flew around the room only saying boo!
Whoop-de-doo!
That was fun.
But we weren't done.
So we flew around the house.
Then we saw a mouse.
That gave us such a scare
I thought it was a bear.
So I threw it in the air.
The mouse fell in the pie.
Oh my!
What will happen now?
Then the mouse
ate the pie like a cow.

Holly Hahn

PASSAGE OF TIME AND THOUGHT

Watching lightning flash at night
Looking at it seems so right
The flash and glow, steady rain
As though only sky could be so vain

Looking out the window sill
I'm sitting there, thinking still
Of all the things I do not know
Things I never did let go

And I'm looking at the mirror now
Wondering if I've changed somehow
Or am I still the same young child
With the pretty looks hiding the inner wild?

I used to have such a pretty smile
One thousand watts shining all the while
But now that smile is not the same
Not that different, but something's changed

Is it just the years I've grown?
Or the knowledge of the once unknown?
I miss the things I knew before
This passage of time opened the door

Small things used to matter so much
Now it's just the past I touch
But I am shaped from yesterdays
And so many things I cannot say

I guess I'm still who I was before
But this child became so much more . . .

Ayla Breanne Ault
Age: 16

My dog found a stick,
That was very thick.
The woods have trees,
With many bees.
I walked him in the dark,
While at the park.
He goes wild,
If he sees a child.

Blake McKay
Age: 11

RACECAR

It's the place where I sit that is the most exciting;
It vibrates and roars with the strike of lightning!
It speeds to the finish line without any stops;
It takes me twelve seconds to the eighth mile,
and never drops!
And in my mind I hope I've done it,
And I know I have when my dad says "You've won it!"
And at the end of the race,
When I take my gear off,
I think about the next time I'll take off!

Brandy Protz
Age: 10

THE WIND'S SONG

As the wind blows through my hair
I wonder where it goes
Up through the trees into the skies
Carrying a song with it
A secret no one knows
How desperately I want to know that song
I pray one day the wind will take me to the heavens
And I will hear that song
I wait for that day

Margaret Marie Mumm
Age: 10

BUTTERFLIES WHEN YOU'RE DANCING

Butterflies, butterflies,
everywhere
Filling my stomach
without a care;
My dance is today
so I need to let it shine;
Showing the people
the dance floor is mine;
Hearing the crowd clap,
whistle, and yell,
I now know
that I did well!

Morgan Cripe
Age: 10

GRANDMA

I love my grandmother a lot.
She will always be in my heart.
I wish she were still here
grinning from ear to ear.
I have no fear
because I know she is near
looking down from above
with a heart full of love.

Braley Dietzen
Age: 13

GYMNASTICS

My nerves are running high,
I'm starting to get the butterflies,
Stomach tight, shoulders in, all I want to do is win!
Run, run, run with all your might,
Backflip, frontflip, keep those legs tight,
Point those toes, point those feet, point them hard,
You'll win the meet!
Round off, flip, flop flip, flip, flop,
Oh great, I have to stop;
Stick it, hold it, salute, and smile,
All of a sudden the crowd goes wild!
The scores are high, the trophies given,
All that hard work sure was worth livin'!

Hailey Black
Age: 10

MY BROTHERS

Dayton's little brother is small,
And he really likes to bawl.
Dayton's big brother is tall,
And he really likes to make me fall.
It really doesn't matter whether they are small or tall,
I love them all.

Dayton Lord
Age: 8

ORANGE

What is orange?
Orange is the sky,
Just before dawn . . .
The brief smile of the sunset,
Before the light is gone . . .
Lighter than red,
Yet darker than yellow.
Right in between,
The angry
And the mellow . . .
Perfectly in the middle you see?
The perfect mix,
Of salty and sweet.
Orange is the sun,
Muffled by the night,
When the moon begins to fight for its right.
Orange is beautiful . . .
My favorite color at best,
I take pity on those
Who call it a "color pest."
Probably the color
That is most unforlorned
All of the above
Describe the color
Orange . . .

Mikella C. Marley
Age: 11

I saw a ghost.
Who was a host.
He saw a post.
Most ghosts like toast.
Most ghosts are hosts.
Ghosts like beef roast.
He lives on the coast.

Madison Fox
Age: 6

MY GOAT LIZY

Lizy is my pet goat.
She wears a white and brown coat.
Lizy walks around on her lead rope all day.
She doesn't like it when I go away.

Kirby Herrmann
Age: 10

BASEBALL

I
love baseball
a lot. It is lots of
fun to me because when
you are up to bat there is so
much adrenaline, especially
in a championship game.
I love being in that position
because it makes me
feel like a hero!

Mitch Trees
Age: 11

FLY

I would like to fly,
with the birds above,
I would fly real high,
soar like a dove.

I would love to fly,
touch treetops,
fly high in the sky,
'til the wind stops.

Nicole B. Miller
Age: 10

SUBSTITUTES

There is my substitute,
she is mean and not so cute.
When she comes in,
I thought I saw a dinosaur.
Either way it doesn't matter,
all I hear from her is chatter, chatter.
When that dinosaur came
I fell asleep and snored
and she whacked me to stay awake.
If that's mean wait and see
what our regular teacher will be.

Kaylee Melton
Age: 10

I'M AN ATHLETE

Sports is my best thing to do,
I go outside to play soccer too.
All sports are part of me.
Can't you see,
That I love them all.
I hate the mall.
I'd rather be playing softball.
I love every sport I do.

McKenna Burt
Age: 10

Wet drops of wonder
We don't know what to think of it
Where does it come from?
How does it stop?
What exactly is it?
No one knows how to stop it
We don't even know what it's called
We watch it come and go by
Until we see gray clouds pass us
And when the golden sun peeks out
Yet we still don't know what it's called
Until the day sweet nature whispers in our ear
"This is the rain"

Jordan Minder
Age: 11

UNCLE!?

You should meet my uncle.
But he's not so sweet.
If that's bad, compare that to his feet!
He eats all day and he eats all night!
But his booming voice makes a fright!
He wears the '70s fashion fad.
What . . . you say that is Dad?
Oh well I'm going out to play!

Payne Nicholas Kerz
Age: 10

MATH

math class I hate it so
boring tough and rough
sit through it every day
hate it in every way
do the problems
so hard
I must use a calculator
wanting to do it later
wanting to take a nap
wanting to eat a snack
wanting to escape
from the math class
draw in my notebook
look at the clock, long time left
stare at the board
get so confused
scream in horror
in the math class
why must I do it!
why must I go through it!
why do I have to suffer every day
in the math class
I am bored out of my mind
leaving myself behind
zoning out
into my math-free world
then I hear a shout
and I come out
into a math-filled world
filled with problems here and there

math everywhere
there is no escaping
from the math class
look at the clock, much more to go
in my mind I scream and shout
oh please let me out!
let me be free!
let me escape!
from the math class
teacher calls on me
I don't have a clue
she frowns
she scowls
she calls on someone else
then she says "math is over."
and I thank the Lord
I am safe from the math class

Gina Moroff
Age: 12

TOYS 'R' US

When it's snowing and cold,
I like to go there in the evening,
To see the Bratz and babies,
To hear the bunnies hopping,
While I run up and down the aisles!
I will go there again next weekend
And that makes me smile!

Persephone R. Robinson
Age: 6

YELLOW

Yellow is a happy color.
It's also the color of my butter.
Yellow is a blooming flower,
Even if it's on a tower.
Yellow's sound is Ha, Ha, Ha!
And if you sing, it's La, La, La!
Yellow is a colored pencil.
Please, use it on a sun-shaped stencil.
It's also Wal-Mart's little icon.
I'm sure glad it's not a python!

Cameron Moore
Age: 9

MOM

The pain I feel inside is strong
Are my feelings right or wrong?
I've tried to determine how I feel
Are my feelings fake or real?
I still don't know what to do
I'm not a full person without you
I miss you so, my beloved mom

In loving memory of Debbie Anne Stowers

Chastidy Paige Campbell
Age: 13

PINK

Pink is fun
Like swimming in the sun.
Pink is sweet
Like the slippers
On Cam's feet . . .
Pink is sad
When my dog is being bad
And the color
Is taking over
The face of my dad . . .
Pink is the color
Of Cate's skin
So she likes to dine
And go for a swim . . .

Ingrid Hoogland
Age: 11

DOGS

Dogs
bark, run
sniffing, jumping, licking
I just love dogs.
Man's best friend

Logan Hilgenbrink
Age: 8

THE FIRST DAY OF SCHOOL

The first day of school is such a rush.
I have to brush my teeth, brush my hair,
New shoes galore, new hairdos
"Mom, I wonder what I will do.
What if my teacher is mean or strict?"

I wonder if my friends are going to be there?
What if my desk is in front so I can't throw wads
into the mean people's hair?
I wonder if I will get detention like I did last year?
I wonder if I can create an explosion that will cause fear?

But, the thing I'm scared of the most is getting an F+++,
like I did last year,
And I'm also scared of getting an A+++,
because my mom will hug me and call me "dear."
My mom said if I don't fail grade three like I have before,
she would get me a horse and take me to the store.

I'm still worried because today I'm an hour late.
What if I get sent to the principal's office on my first
day?
When I got to school,
my new teacher was pointing that way,
I headed to the office, much to my dismay.

I received a red card, which meant after-school detention,
What a great way, on my first day,
to get my mom's attention!

Anna Benoit
Age: 8

NORTHERN EAGLE

Northern eagle in the sky,
Northern eagle hunting fish,
Northern eagle fly back home soon.

Zachary Loyd
Age: 8

HORSES

A horse, an animal, a creature.
The heart of the mountains.
The soul of the west.
What to my surprise a horse.
People construct, kill, and destroy the prairies.
The homes of the wild horses.
The rich are bored.
The wild are free.
Not many people care for the wild horses.
Me I care.
A horse, an animal, a creature
The west, the prairie
My soul, the wild horses.

Lauryl Hassen
Age: 11

BLUE

The sky is blue and you have a clue,
You drew a picture with glue,
And got all gluey when you drew with glue.

Most of the world is blue—
The oceans and lakes are blue,
And the sky is blue, too!

I wear jeans that are blue,
Shirts of the same hue,
And every day, I wear shoes of blue.

Lesley McLafferty
Age: 8

MY DOG

My dog was in the log and now my dog is in some clogs.
My dog's name is Gilly. He is quite silly!
My dog is in my pool to keep cool.
My dog hangs on bars, so he is a star.
My dog got a rat, the rat said "don't be a brat."
My dog got a bunny. He thinks he's funny, and he is.

Molly Budinger
Age: 6

FALL

Fall is full of color
The colors red, orange, and brown
Fall is always fun

Sydney Lynch
Age: 10

OH PRESIDENTS

Oh Presidents, oh, Presidents
What have you done?

Ronald Reagan was shot, but did not die-
Three others did die and we may never know why.

FDR gave us the "New Deal,"
And Van Buren promised things for votes—

Jefferson made a purchase,
And the "Emancipation Proclamation" Abe wrote.

Your job is to take care of us and keep us informed,
To keep us safe and send our troops to war—

When I grow up, President I want to be—
So I can do these things for my country!

Kristina Lewis
Age: 9

Pink is . . .
girls, suckers,
and juicy strawberries,
love, hearts,
and blossoms in the spring,
strength, joy,
and happiness,
love for my mom
'cause she is the very best,
peace, friends,
and breast cancer ribbons,
a Valentine's Day card
that is being written,
red, white,
and all of the above,
this poem's dedicated to my mom
'cause she gives me love.

Missy DeMarco
Age: 10

EAGLE

The big bird of prey,
With a big white head,
Big sharp talons,
And a big hooked beak—
The eagle.

Alec Sullivan
Age: 8

What does love mean to the weary soul?
Kindness in the heart, or being free?
But the number one question is how can it find us?
How does it hunt us down?
The obvious answer is, it is forever with us,
the bad and the kind of heart.
It is with us if we want it to be or not.

Who could imagine the world without love?
The truth is nobody can.
If the world were without love this would not be a world.

Here it is time for my leave,
good-bye and remember what I say!

Kaitlin L. Atterbury
Age: 11

LEAVES

Leaves, leaves, the wonder of leaves,
They fall off the trees—

They could be yellow, red, or green,
But when it is fall, they might even be brown leaves—

Leaves, leaves in the fall, you might be raked up,
So bye-bye leaves of all different colors.

Alexis Power
Age: 7

SONG OF FIRE

Warm embers glow
Warm embers friend to all
Source of light
Source of light glowing bright.

From fire we are nourished
Nourished, we will grow
Source of light
Source of light glowing bright.

Warm winds blow
Warm winds blow, breathing life
Source of light
Source of light glowing bright.

Blazing fire clears the land
Blazing fire makes way for new
Source of light
Source of light glowing bright.

Dillon Bean
Age: 10

FALL

In the fall the game is on
And Mom and Dad are always gone
Harvesting crops all day long
As I rake leaves and sing a song.

And cooler weather comes around
As pumpkins lay on the ground
While we go shopping for warmer clothes
And pretty scarves to warm our nose.

There's Halloween and trick-or-treating
Then Thanksgiving and eat, eat, eating
That sweet and delicious pumpkin pie
And the juicy turkey, my oh my!

These are the things
I love about fall
I bet you too
Love them all!

Heather Kuberski
Age: 11

MISCHIEVOUS CREATURE

Dragon so fire-hot
Dragon so great and mighty
Mischievous creature

Corey Meskil
Age: 10

BLACK

Black is a zebra,
Without its white stripes,
Black is dirty, gross pipes
Black is headphones
And chocolate ice cream cones,
Black is the annoying pencil sharpener,
I would much rather be
Swinging with my partner,
Black is the lines of a ruler,
And Riley says she's way cooler,
Black is Mikella's tights,
My dog had to go to the groomer,
(Because he had black tiny mites)
Black is the radio,
And my brother's stereo,
What would you do without black?
All I know is that I would lack!

Cate Buescher
Age: 9

A FISH TALE

My sister got a brand-new fish.
But now it's dead (not what she'd wish.)
Sis wouldn't eat a thing in her dish.
I tried to tell her sorry for killing that fish.

I thought it wanted a bubble bath.
(I really didn't do the math.)
I poured a lot of bubbles in.
And now I know it was a sin.

I was only two or three.
Now I wish that you would see.
What I did caused a lot of sorrow.
But just like Scarlet, I'll think about it tomorrow.

Sydney Redman
Age: 10

AT CHUCK E. CHEESE

When it's warm and sunny
I like to go there on Saturdays.
To see Chuck E. Cheese smiling
To hear kids laughing.
While I eat pepperoni pizza.
I will go there again next month
And that makes me smile!

Ava Charneice Lee
Age: 7

LOST

When you're lost
In the rain
Nobody's around you
All you can see is the light from the streetlights
You can't go anywhere but home
Your mind's a-rumblin'
Your heart's tellin' you to go
What do you do?
Do you go?
Or do you stand—alone in the dark?

Courtney Shae Meskil
Age: 14

MY BEST FRIEND

Cheyenne Helmers, my best friend,
You moved to Alaska on a rainy day,
People might not know you,
But I do.
I know you can't come back,
But I wish you could.
I miss you, so do your friends, and my Girl Scout troop.
You left in third grade,
But I want you to come back today.

Ellie Buntenbach
Age: 9

FACELESS LOVE

One plain day while talking to a friend
your voice came over the phone
and that's when it began,
So many times in the past my heart had been broke,
yet my troubles would leave me whenever you spoke.
I felt a connection, though I had never seen your face,
and the happiest times were when we talked real late.
Though time and buildings have kept us apart,
one day we'll find each other
while being led by our hearts.
That day our hands will lace and our lips will connect,
and it will be a magical meeting with firework effects.
While God and angels smile from above,
our blind eyes will see,
and it will no longer be a faceless love.

Jennifer Yates
Age: 15

MY FRIEND

My friend is like a creature
I'm afraid he will eat my teacher
My friend is a menace
But does like to play tennis
My friend sleeps on his head
I don't think he has ever heard of a bed

Nicholas Gab
Age: 10

135

WHY DO WE FIGHT?

A mother and her daughter
sit at night and pray
for their loved ones in the war
the ones that went away.
They talk about how they miss them
and how they love them so
and how they wish
they didn't have to go.
When they finish
the daughter gives a weary smile
and says I don't want to go to war
and leave you for a while.
Because I know how much it hurts
when you don't know when they'll come back
and wait for letters and phone calls
just to keep your love intact.
Mommy I don't understand
why they go to war
when all they do is hurt someone
or give themselves a sore.
But I do understand that they fight for our country
and try to do what's right
trying to keep their families safe
not trying to stir up a fight.
For that I'll never give up on them
for doing what they think's best
It's not giving up on them
is the hardest test.

With that her mother nodded
having a tear in her eye
I hope you'll give your best
and always keep your head high.

Shaina Marie Lloyd
Age: 13

YOUR YOUNGER SIBLINGS

Oh your younger siblings,
they don't know what to do,
they can be weird,
their favorite color is blue.

They think they can fly,
but give them a chance,
they "fly" in circles,
but really they just dance.

Oh your younger siblings,
they are so exciting,
they give you hugs and kisses,
then later you are fighting.

Breyaniah Leigh Noble
Age: 10

THERE ONCE WAS A BUNNY

There once was a bunny named Snickers
Who thought he had very big whiskers.
So he stayed put in his dome, which he calls his home,
So nobody could ever see him.
One day at the bay was this very special day
Where bunnies can meet.
When he got there he was embarrassed
Until he saw a bunny with very big feet.

Brittney Harrington
Age: 11

NUTCRACKER

Nutcracker, nutcracker under the tree;
A special present Santa brought to me;
Now, I have twenty;
My dad says that's plenty!
But I hope each year Santa is dear
and keeps putting them under the tree for me.

Connor Eyman
Age: 11

IT STARTS WITH ME

I wanna dance within a rainbow,
I wanna jump inside the sun,
I wanna leap from cloud to cloud,
Because my days on Earth are done.
I wanna go where there will be no war,
I wanna walk amongst where angels soar.

I'd love to speak to the Man who controls my life,
I'd love to share with Him my everlasting life.

To make this happen . . .

I must share my love with all of my friends,
I must stick with Him until the end.
I must appreciate every passing day,
I must listen to what they have to say.
In order to be everlasting and free,
I must know—IT STARTS WITH ME!

Sandi N. Green
Age: 15

D ucks fly
U sally they swim
C an eat bread
K indly stare at you when you have bread

Milene Goodman
Age: 9

GHOST

G hosts are scary
H ow do they fly?
O n a cloud or in the sky
S ometimes spooky sometimes sweet
T hey need to sweep

Bradlyn B. Barnard
Age: 9

SLIDES

S ome things are different.
L ots of people like slides.
I t is fun.
D o you like slides?
E very slide is connected to something.
S ome of them are high.

Callie Block
Age: 8

DOGS

D o tricks
O ften loud
G oing to be crazy
S ometimes bite

Meredith Richards
Age: 8

THE BOUNCY BALL

I had a bouncy ball
It bounced off the wall
The wall was tall

The ball was small
I got a call
While I was chasing the bouncy ball

Brittany Niemann
Age: 9

HALLOWEEN

Things are very scary!
  Lots of candy to carry!
Maybe a gift bag or two!
  I would like to trick-or-treat you!
I have a cool costume!
  And a decorated room!

Sidney A. Eckleberry
Age: 8

LEAVES

Leaves falling left and right

It is such a beautiful sight
It's midnight, such a silent night . . .
      But one noise . . .
         The leaves rustling . . .

    The noise of the silent night goes on.

Alexis Fulcher
Age: 10

MAKING SNOW ANGELS IN MY FRONT YARD

When it's cold and snowing
I like to go there in winter
to see the snowmen
to hear the snowplows
While I lie down in the snow and make snow angels.
I will go there again next winter
and that makes me smile!

Trevor Joseph Akers
Age: 6

AT THE HOLIDAY INN

When it's sunny and hot
I like to go there in summer.
To see the hot tub,
To hear the ice machine,
While I swim in the pool!
I will go there again next summer,
And that makes me smile!

Ian Michael Stearns
Age: 6

AT THE PARK

When it's sunny and chilly,
I like to go there in the morning.
To see the leaves changing colors,
To hear the wind blowing,
While I swing on the swings!
I will go there again next fall
And that makes me smile!

Drew Mikaela Cloud
Age: 7

ADJECTIVES

Unique, smart, nice, and cool,
  describes the people of our school.
Fun, interesting, and all the above,
  are all the things I especially love.
Dependable, trustworthy, also sweet,
  the best friendship that can't be beat.

Tyler Yoho
Age: 10

THE ANIMAL KINGDOM

Some are hairy, some are scary
Some are fearful, some are cheerful
Some are small, and some are tall
Some are cute, some are cuddly
But most of all, they are all animals!

Matthew Simonson
Age: 10

AT THE ZOO

When it's warm and sunny,
I like to go there in summer,
To see the tigers pouncing,
To hear the monkeys chatter,
While I run on the sidewalk.
I will go there again next month,
And that makes me smile!

Sydney Leigh McMakin
Age: 7

FIVE GHOSTS AND GOBLINS

Ghosts and goblins hiding outside.
One of the ghosts said, "Oh my, it's getting late."
Second one said, "Witches in the air."
Third one said, "We don't care."
Fourth one said, "Let's go and have some fun!"
Fifth one said, "Let's go and have some pizza."
And the goblins ran away.

Mason Reiff
Age: 7

BASKETBALL

The score's
a tie! My nerves
are quite high. Dribble,
dribble, and swish. We
make the winning shot!
The crowd goes wild;
Boy, we're hot!

Josie Summann
Age: 10

WITCH

The witch
just had to snitch
a wonderful dish
of fish to give
to the prince to make
him not so tense.

Andrew Lagerhausen
Age: 10

W.T.C. 9/11

There's one day every year in our lives
that we will always remember.
That day happens to be the 11th
and the month is September.
We won't forget the police officers and firefighters
that sacrificed their lives
or the loved ones that have died.
So when this day comes back around, trust me,
we will always remember the eleventh of September.

Chad David Karch
Age: 16

GRANDMA

My grandma
Is nice to me
Every hour of the day
Everywhere
Because she loves me.

Ariel Pryor
Age: 8

MY FRIEND BREKKEN

B est friend.
R esponsible.
E agle-smart.
K indhearted.
K ids me.
E nergetic.
N ever sad.

Dakota Cross
Age: 9

VICTORIA

Artistic, athletic, quiet, bold
Sibling of Jessica and Erin
Lover of cats, music, and writing
Who feels content, happy, and peaceful
Who fears war, death, and losing friends
Who needs God, guidance, and family
Who gives help, encouragement and love
Who would like to see the Swiss Alps,
  A peaceful lake in the mountains,
  And a beautiful beach (not cluttered with litter
  and hurricane debris)
Resident of Small Town, U.S.A.

Victoria Anne Youngs
Age: 12

PICKLES

Pickles
sour, juicy
eat at every meal
every day as often as I can
because I like them
Cucumbers

Emily Mast
Age: 8

GRANDMA'S LEGACY
My Grandmother's Last Words Of Wisdom To Me

As my grandmother lies dying in bed
I stand nearby listening to what she said
My eyes hold tears I try not to show
My grandma smiles,
For there wasn't much she doesn't know.

Baby girl, don't you worry at all about me,
Forever you will keep me in your memory
For I have lived to a rather ripe, old age
But compare it to a storybook,
For each day has a new page.

"You'll end up facing challenges, don't give up hope,"
she said, "just use your heart to make decisions,
and you'll always cope.
One must be strong with success and strife
I know this now from my experiences in life.

You'll have many choices you'll have to make,
And, yes, baby, many times your heart will break.
Despite the pain and tears, your heart will always heal.
Never give in to temptation, don't let yourself steal

Listen to my words, my only granddaughter,
they are true.
These are the things when I was your age I wish I knew"
With a slight smile and a squeeze of my hand
My grandmother hoped to make me understand.

I kissed her gently as she slowly closed her eyes,
And with my grandma's last wisdom in my heart,
I said my last good-bye.

Shalinda Jackson

Mrs. Adcock, Mrs. Adcock
She is my teacher . . .
She is kind to me.
She helps me with my work.
Mrs. Adcock plays fun games with us.
Mrs. Adcock reads us stories.
We take tests for AR.
We take tests for spelling, social studies, and science.
She is kind and fun with us.
We do fun things together.
And she is my teacher for the year!

Mara Plocher
Age: 9

LEAVING ALL AROUND

It's almost been a year since you've died
and nothing is the same,
everybody is different and everything has changed.
Why did you go and leave everyone who cared,
especially when it's so unfair.
I miss you so much,
I wish you could see
that I love you with all my memories.
I hope you are happy wherever you may be,
even though it's not here with me.

Rachel R. Frashier
Age: 17

THANKSGIVING DAY

Fall is here my favorite time of the year,
Leaves are falling off the trees
And there is a slight breeze.

Hooray! Hooray! It's Thanksgiving Day,
Time to cook the turkey
So I don't have to eat beef jerky.

Heather Jarvis
Age: 10

ALL I GOT

I dribble left, I dribble right
I play it day or night
I shoot the long I shoot the short
I love to play this sport
Sometimes against friends sometimes not
Whoever it is I'll give it all I've got

Collin Young
Age: 11

MIDNIGHT SKY

The stars the moon the midnight sky
Looking down at everything
The sun went down
The moon comes out
The stars glitter in the sky
The moon shines out bright
Soon the sun will rise
The moon will leave
The stars will go
The day will come
The day will go
Then the midnight sky will come
The moon the stars the midnight sky shining bright

Paisley Jane Stewart
Age: 11

BASEBALL

Baseball is like a new morning day.
Each game reminds me of a rising sun,
making me feel fresh and ready to play.
Every time I suit up for the game,
it reminds me of a new day.

For each game means
another chance to become a star.
Not a star that comes out at night
but the star I become in my game.

As I step up to the plate
swinging for the fences,
praying for some distance.
With a mighty swing I fling the ball
going over the wall, ending my day right.

Dylan Mikal Jett
Age: 11

Me and my cousins are here and there.
We go four-wheeler-riding everywhere.
We play tag at dark.
Then our parents get mad and we have to park.

Aiden McMahan

THE WORLD ENDED TODAY

The world ended today
In what way, you say?
A tornado blew through L.A.
As weird as it may seem
Hurricanes just rolled through Indiana
Alaska had a snowstorm
Arizona had a snowstorm
But even a snowstorm was in Tampa Bay
So the world ended today

Megan Elizabeth Jackson
Age: 11

BIG COUSIN

I'm a big cousin to three,
It is a hard job you see,
The girl really makes it hard,
She is such a drama queen,
The boys always want to wrestle,
But it is who they are,
And at the end of every day I love them,
I'm a big cousin who's proud of her younger three.

Mary Stanfield
Age: 12

NEPHEWS

I am the older aunt of four boys.
The older two don't like to share toys.
You see, I can't believe that I have two more.

The youngests are babies who cry all the time.
So I'm not surprised when the older two act as mimes.

Since I am the oldest, I am sometimes left
To take care of the older two.
It's a huge responsibility but only given to a few.

There are many advantages to having nephews.
It makes me feel special when they say,
     "I love you."

Mariah Teriet
Age: 11

THE BLUE SKY

I see the blue sky
Above me very high.
The fluffy clouds float by.
I watch them and I do a little sigh.
I feel so relaxed when I lie
On the ground to watch the sky.

Sarah Gomez
Age: 8

BABY ANGEL

A baby has passed on.
At the age of one.
God sends an angel all in white.
To help the baby angel
spread his wings and take flight.
He flaps his wings and goes 'round and 'round.
Then suddenly he falls to the ground.
He tries again and tries to fly.
Once again he falls and begins to cry.
She takes his hand and whispers to him
that it will be all right.
She spreads her wings and takes flight.
She takes him to meet the Lord.
where he will always be adored.
Now everything is all right.
Because the baby angel has reached Heaven's light.

Cheyene Smith
Age: 13

PINE TREES

In the bright warm sun
Pine trees blowing in the wind
Fall has started to begin

Skyler Roper
Age: 11

AS THE LEAVES FALL

As I watch the leaves fall
The squirrels gather nuts
And put them into tree trunks
The birds fly in a "V"
As they migrate from here and from me
As the leaves fall
The weather gets colder
The coats come bolder
As the leaves fall
Bears hibernate
Butterflies migrate
As the snow falls
The lakes are frozen
The snow blowers blowin'
The salt is shakin'
While the turkey is bakin'
As the snow falls white covers everything
While family comes pouring in
As the flowers pop up
The birds come home
Bees buzzing making a honeycomb
As the flowers pop up
The poppies and daisies so colorful and bright
As the sun is bright swimming pools are full
The green grass is cool
As the sun is bright

The toes show through flip-flops
Lemonade stands next to ice-cream shops
Then it starts to get colder
As the leaves fall

Caitlyn Sanders
Age: 11

TRYOUT BLUES

Pompoms and ponytails
Lots of many screams
Sweaty arms and lots of fear
Oh golly just to cheer!!

After it's all over
Your fear will disappear
But hold on to your britches
There's a do-over next school year

Emma Elizabeth Creel
Age: 11

BUBBLEGUM

Chewy, fun, Pop goes the bubblegum!
Pop! Pop! Pop! everywhere;
Bubblegum is in the air.

Austin Metzger
Age: 11

Fight
harsh, rugged
attacking, impacting, rushing
squabble, riot, calm, mute
relaxing, reposing, napping
neat, tidy
Tranquil

Ian Duncan Holsapple
Age: 11

FALLING

I built a wall around my heart.
No one was getting in.
I wasn't gonna get too close.
I wasn't going through love again.

I thought it was gonna be easy.
I thought that I could resist,
but I just couldn't fight love off.
The feelings are too strong when we kiss.

I tried so hard not to fall in love.
I knew if I did, I'd get hurt,
but as the days went on it got clearer and clearer
that trying not to love you didn't work.

I fought with my heart every day.
I tried so hard to keep you out,
but you just keep on loving me.
You finally broke through, no doubt.

A part of me is still scared to death;
a part of me still thinks you'll leave.
I still have a lot of fear inside,
but I guess all I can do is believe . . .

Believe that you won't hurt me,
and trust you with all my heart,
'cause it's too late . . . I'm too far gone;
if you left, I'd fall apart.

Karly R. Parker
Age: 16

I'D RATHER . . .

Be a dog than a slimy old frog.
I'd rather be a cat than a measly little rat.
I'd rather be a bee than a tiny flea.
I'd rather eat a lime than drink a bunch of slime.
I'd rather bake a thousand cakes
  just as long as I'm not a snake!

Breanna Nimmo

FRIENDSHIP . . .

Friendship is someone who shares.
Friendship is someone who cares.
Friendship can last a lifetime or just a little while
but you always share a smile.
If you ever find a friendship like mine
cherish it for a lifetime.

Anna Joy Migliore
Age: 10

A FAMILY'S LOVE

Death has come once again.
To take her out of pain.
To many death is a bad thing,
but it is a good thing.
Death takes pain away.
She is up in Heaven.
She is doing all she couldn't before.
She is smiling and laughing.
She is with her family.
She is watching over her
grandchildren.
She is better off.
NO MORE PAIN.
NO MORE CANCER.
NO MORE SUFFERING.
Only happiness from now on for her.
She loved us dearly.
She would want the best for us.
She is without pain.
Without cancer now.
Seeing her in the pain she was in,
hurt dearly.
See death can be good.
Death has come and gone once again,
but for a good reason.
Death can be good at times.

In loving memory:
Carmen Reynolds (Grandma, Great Me-Ma)

Amber Reynolds
Age: 16

FALL

Autumn reminds me of . . .
Big, fat, bright orange pumpkins for Halloween
Fun hayrides in the dark
At my mom's boss' Halloween party
Hearing people scream at Halloween haunted houses
Milk chocolate and bitter SweeTARTS
Wearing a scary costume on Halloween night
Windy, cool, rainy, soggy, and wet weather

Hayley Michel
Age: 8

The dancer twirled after she got her hair curled.
Going on stage in your gown, she fainted down.
Pink, purple, and blue,
is all she could find to match her shoe.
The audience clapped loud,
and she felt like she was floating on a cloud.
She got first place,
and beet-red got her face.
If nothing got in her way,
she knew she won today.

Brittny J. Williams

Bats
Bite, bite, bite
Banana bread, bluebirds,
And big bones!

Niklas C. Landgraf
Age: 7

A THANK YOU NOTE TO GOD

Mother
She cuddles with me.

Father
He plays with me.

Colin
He lets me play with him.

Benjamin
He licks me.

Thank You God
For all of these!

Abby Bloeser
Age: 7

CRAZY BAT

Big head
Skinny body
Long wings
Small feet
Night-flyer
Bug-eater
Cave-dweller

Logan Moore
Age: 8

Bats
furry, neat
flying, squeaking, hanging
interested, scared, happy, fascinated
Awesome animal

Shayla Hinson
Age: 8

There once was a boy named Joe
Who had a big fat toe
It got in the way
When he was trying to play
So Joe said this toe has to go

Jacob Maddox
Age: 10

AIRPORT

I like the airport.
The people at the airport gave me wings
To clip on shirts.
The plane went to Florida.
When I got back,
I clipped the wings on my shirt.

Brandon Palmer
Age: 8

IF I WERE IN CHARGE OF THE WORLD

If I were in charge of the world
I'd cancel cheese sandwiches
Cold weather, snakes,
And also my brother.

If I were in charge of the world
There'd be more schooltime.
Birthdays all year long,
And more desserts

If I were in charge of the world
You wouldn't have the word "no."
You wouldn't have rainy days.
You wouldn't have bumblebee stings.
Or jellyfish stings.
You wouldn't even have jellyfish!

If I were in charge of the world.
Nothing would bite.
Every movie would be PG or G.
And a person who sometimes forgets
To keep her room neat
Would still be allowed to be
In charge of the world.

Tara Jolley
Age: 9